All Through the Night

The publisher gratefully acknowledges the kind permission granted to reprint the following copyrighted material. Should any copyright holder have been inadvertently omitted, they should apply to the publisher, who will be pleased to credit them in full in any subsequent editions.

Louis Weber, C.E.O.
Publications International, Ltd.
7373 North Cicero Avenue
Lincolnwood, Illinois 60646

ISBN: 0-7853-3905-1

All Through the Night

Adapted by Lynne Suesse

Cover illustrated by Judith Pfeiffer, Linda Prater

Interior illustrated by
Judith Pfeiffer, Tish Tenud,
Linda Howard

Publications International, Ltd.

In my little bed I lie,
  God, my Father, hear my cry;
Please protect me through the night,
  Keep me safe till morning light.
Amen.

Good night! Good night!
  Far flies the light;
But still in God's love
  Shall flame above,
Making all bright.
  Good night! Good night!

Victor Hugo

Dear God,

Sometimes when I look outside my window, I see tiny blinking lights. Mommy says they're fireflies, but I think they're angels coming to say, "Good night!"

Sleep, my child,
  And peace attend thee,
All through the night;
  Guardian angels
God will send thee,
  All through the night.

Night Blessing

Good night,
　Sleep tight,
Wake up bright
　In the morning light
To do what's right
　With all your might.
Amen.

14

Jesus said: "Do not worry about tomorrow, for tomorrow will worry about itself. Each day has enough trouble of its own."

Matthew 6:34

Be near me, Lord Jesus;
  I ask Thee to stay
Close by me forever,
  And love me, I pray;
Bless all the dear children
  in Thy tender care,
And fit us for heaven
  To live with Thee there.

17

18

Evening Hymn

I hear no voice, I feel no touch,
  I see no glory bright;
But yet I know that God is near,
  In darkness as in light.

Lord, keep us safe this night,
  Secure from all our fears.
May angels guard us
  while we sleep,
  Till morning light appears.

The moon shines bright,
  The stars give light
Before the break of day;
  God bless you all,
Both great and small,
  And send a joyful day.

Angels at the foot,
    And angels at the head,
And like a curly little lamb,
    My pretty babe in bed.

Amen.